sunday school planner

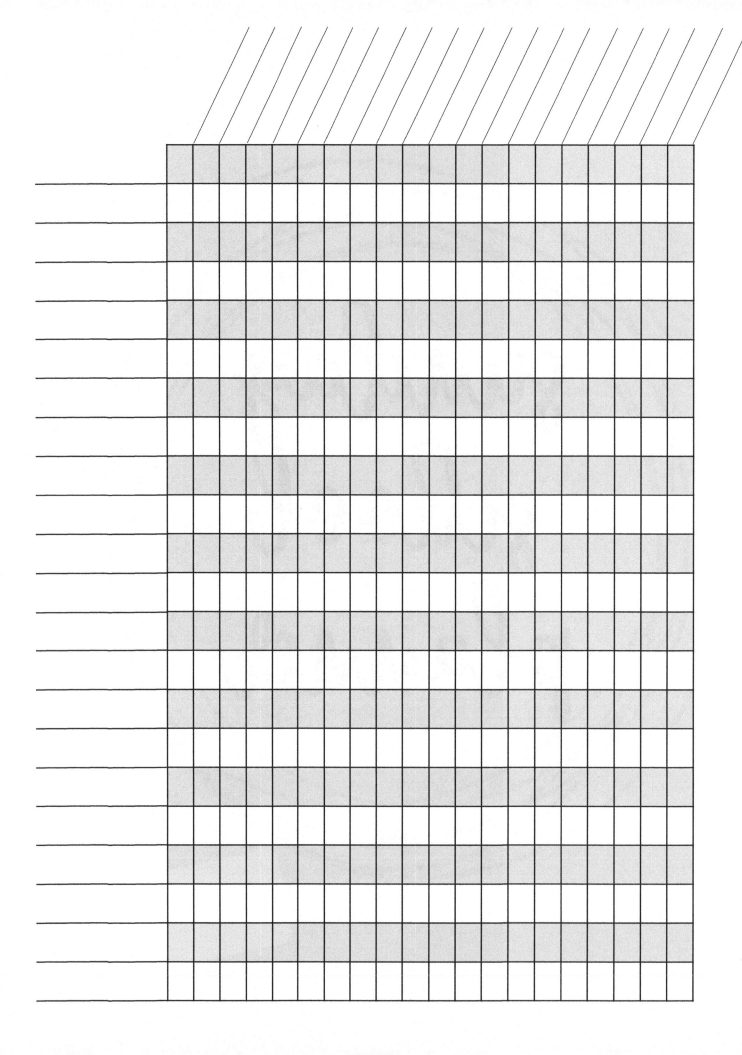

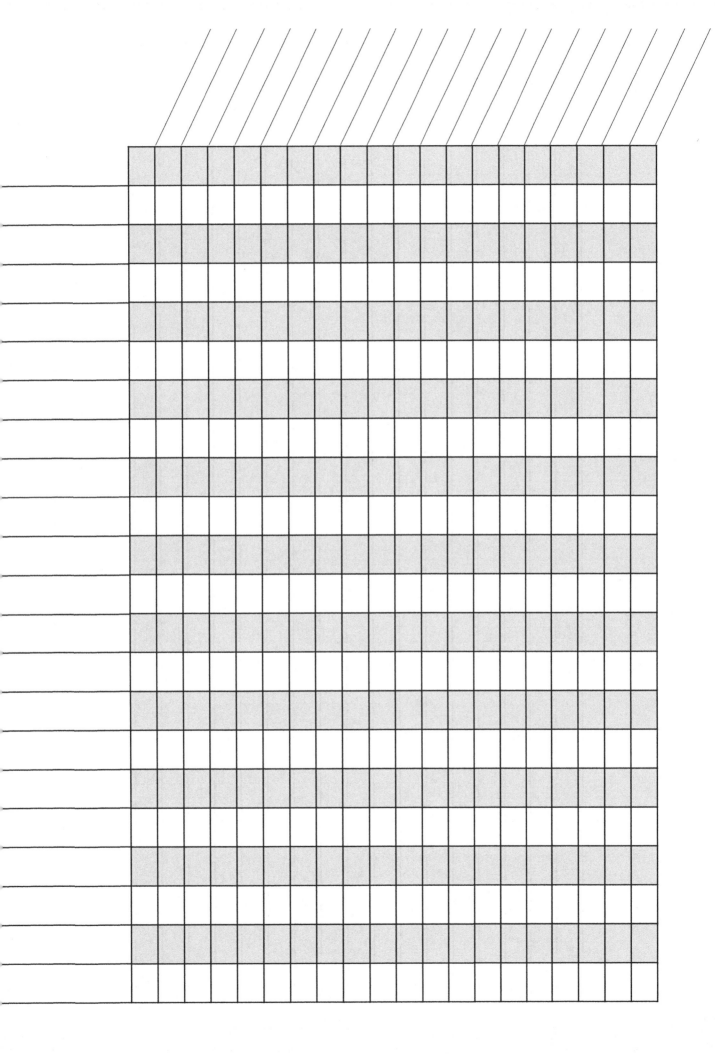

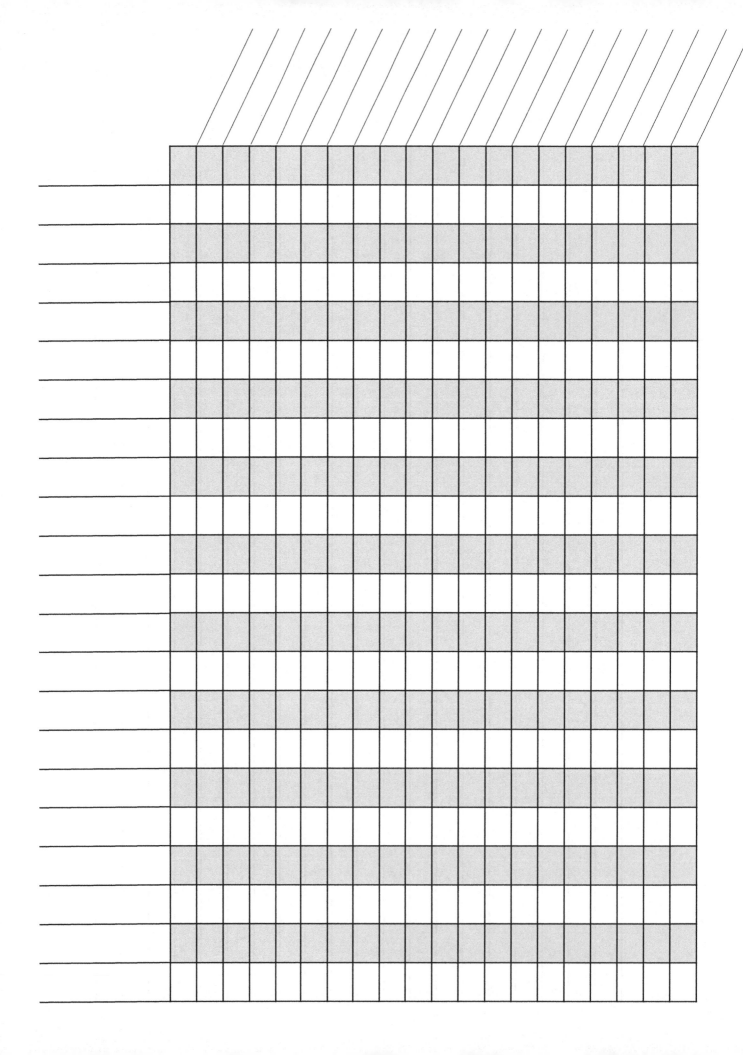

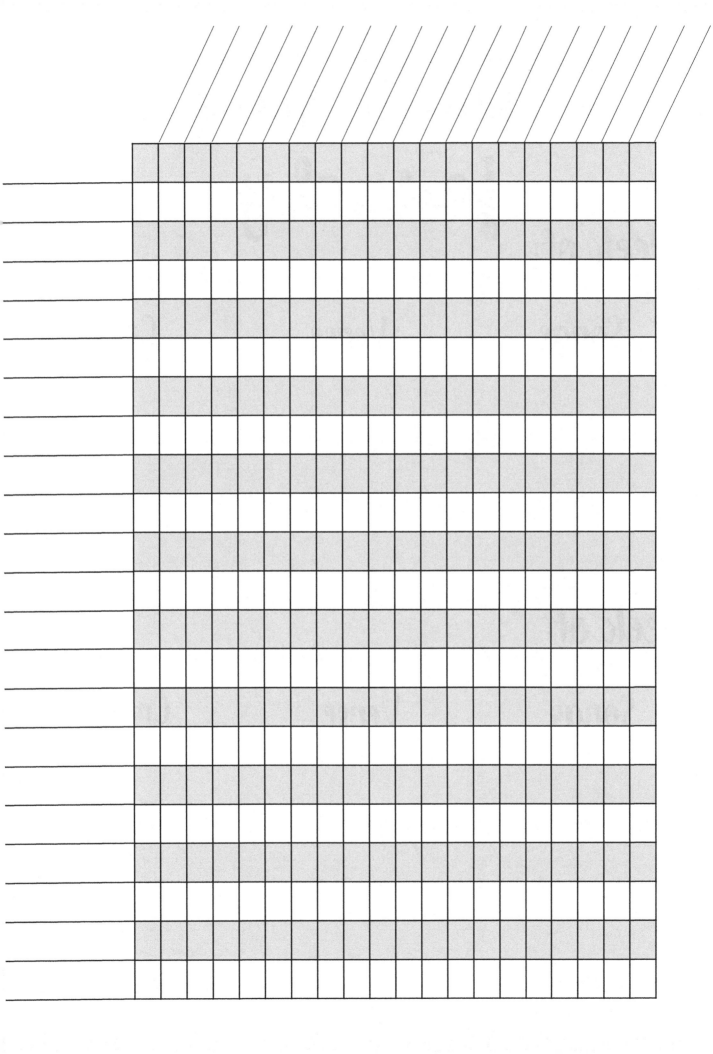

year at a glance

january

Week of:

Songs	Verse	Craft

Week of:

Songs	Verse	Craft

year at a glance

january

Week of:

Songs	Verse	Craft

Week of:

Songs	Verse	Craft

year at a glance
january

Week of:

Songs	Verse	Craft

Week of:

Songs	Verse	Craft

year at a glance
february

Week of:

Songs	Verse	Craft

Week of:

Songs	Verse	Craft

year at a glance
february

Week of:

Songs	Verse	Craft

Week of:

Songs	Verse	Craft

year at a glance
february

Week of:

Songs	Verse	Craft

Week of:

Songs	Verse	Craft

year at a glance

march

Week of:

Songs	Verse	Craft

Week of:

Songs	Verse	Craft

march

Week of:

Songs	Verse	Craft

Week of:

Songs	Verse	Craft

year at a glance
march

Week of:

Songs	Verse	Craft

Week of:

Songs	Verse	Craft

year at a glance

april

Week of:

Songs	Verse	Craft

Week of:

Songs	Verse	Craft

year at a glance
april

Week of:

Songs	Verse	Craft

Week of:

Songs	Verse	Craft

year at a glance
april

Week of:

Songs	Verse	Craft

Week of:

Songs	Verse	Craft

year at a glance

may

Week of:

Songs	Verse	Craft

Week of:

Songs	Verse	Craft

year at a glance

may

Week of:

Songs	Verse	Craft

Week of:

Songs	Verse	Craft

year at a glance

may

Week of:

Songs	Verse	Craft

Week of:

Songs	Verse	Craft

year at a glance

june

Week of:

Songs	Verse	Craft

Week of:

Songs	Verse	Craft

year at a glance
june

Week of:

Songs	Verse	Craft

Week of:

Songs	Verse	Craft

year at a glance
june

Week of:

Songs	Verse	Craft

Week of:

Songs	Verse	Craft

year at a glance

july

Week of:

Songs	Verse	Craft

Week of:

Songs	Verse	Craft

year at a glance
july

Week of:

Songs	Verse	Craft

Week of:

Songs	Verse	Craft

year at a glance

july

Week of:

Songs	Verse	Craft

Week of:

Songs	Verse	Craft

year at a glance
august

Week of:

Songs	Verse	Craft

Week of:

Songs	Verse	Craft

year at a glance

august

Week of:

Songs	Verse	Craft

Week of:

Songs	Verse	Craft

year at a glance
august

Week of:

Songs	Verse	Craft

Week of:

Songs	Verse	Craft

year at a glance

september

Week of:

Songs	Verse	Craft

Week of:

Songs	Verse	Craft

september

Week of:

Songs	Verse	Craft

Week of:

Songs	Verse	Craft

year at a glance
september

Week of:

Songs	Verse	Craft

Week of:

Songs	Verse	Craft

year at a glance
october

Week of:

Songs	Verse	Craft

Week of:

Songs	Verse	Craft

year at a glance
october

Week of:

Songs	Verse	Craft

Week of:

Songs	Verse	Craft

october

Week of:

Songs	Verse	Craft

Week of:

Songs	Verse	Craft

year at a glance

november

Week of:

Songs	Verse	Craft

Week of:

Songs	Verse	Craft

year at a glance
november

Week of:

Songs	Verse	Craft

Week of:

Songs	Verse	Craft

november

Week of:

Songs	Verse	Craft

Week of:

Songs	Verse	Craft

year at a glance

november

Week of:

Songs	Verse	Craft

Week of:

Songs	Verse	Craft

year at a glance
december

Week of:

Songs	Verse	Craft

Week of:

Songs	Verse	Craft

year at a glance

december

Week of:

Songs	Verse	Craft

Week of:

Songs	Verse	Craft

year at a glance
december

Week of:

Songs	Verse	Craft

Week of:

Songs	Verse	Craft

year at a glance
december

Week of:

Songs	Verse	Craft

Week of:

Songs	Verse	Craft

year at a glance
december

Week of:

Songs	Verse	Craft

Week of:

Songs	Verse	Craft

attendance

Present

Absent

week of:

Songs

Verse

Lesson

Craft and Activity

attendance

Present

Absent

week of:

Songs

Verse

Lesson

Craft and Activity

attendance

Present

Absent

week of:

Songs

Verse

Lesson

Craft and Activity

attendance

Present

Absent

week of:

Songs

Verse

Lesson

Craft and Activity

attendance

Present

Absent

week of:

Songs

Verse

Lesson

Craft and Activity

attendance

Present

Absent

week of:

Songs

Verse

Lesson

Craft and Activity

attendance

Present

Absent

week of:

Songs

Verse

Lesson

Craft and Activity

attendance

Present

Absent

week of:

Songs

Verse

Lesson

Craft and Activity

attendance

Present

Absent

week of:

Songs

Verse

Lesson

Craft and Activity

attendance

Present

Absent

week of:

Songs

Verse

Lesson

Craft and Activity

attendance

Present

Absent

week of:

Songs

Verse

Lesson

Craft and Activity

attendance

Present

Absent

week of:

Songs

Verse

Lesson

Craft and Activity

attendance

Present

Absent

week of:

Songs

Verse

Lesson

Craft and Activity

attendance

Present

Absent

week of:

Songs

Verse

Lesson

Craft and Activity

attendance

Present

Absent

week of:

Songs

Verse

Lesson

Craft and Activity

attendance

Present

Absent

week of:

Songs

Verse

Lesson

Craft and Activity

attendance

Present

Absent

week of:

Songs

Verse

Lesson

Craft and Activity

attendance

Present

Absent

week of:

Songs

Verse

Lesson

Craft and Activity

attendance

Present

Absent

week of:

Songs

Verse

Lesson

Craft and Activity

attendance

Present

Absent

week of:

Songs

Verse

Lesson

Craft and Activity

attendance

Present

Absent

week of:

Songs

Verse

Lesson

Craft and Activity

attendance

Present

Absent

week of:

Songs

Verse

Lesson

Craft and Activity

attendance

Present

Absent

week of:

Songs

Verse

Lesson

Craft and Activity

attendance

Present

Absent

week of:

Songs

Verse

Lesson

Craft and Activity

attendance

Present

Absent

week of:

Songs

Verse

Lesson

Craft and Activity

attendance

Present

Absent

week of:

Songs

Verse

Lesson

Craft and Activity

attendance

Present

Absent

week of:

Songs

Verse

Lesson

Craft and Activity

attendance

Present

Absent

week of:

Songs

Verse

Lesson

Craft and Activity

attendance

Present

Absent

week of:

Songs

Verse

Lesson

Craft and Activity

attendance

Present

Absent

week of:

Songs

Verse

Lesson

Craft and Activity

attendance

Present

Absent

week of:

Songs

Verse

Lesson

Craft and Activity

attendance

Present

Absent

week of:

Songs

Verse

Lesson

Craft and Activity

attendance

Present

Absent

week of:

Songs

Verse

Lesson

Craft and Activity

attendance

Present

Absent

week of:

Songs

Verse

Lesson

Craft and Activity

attendance

Present

Absent

week of:

Songs

Verse

Lesson

Craft and Activity

attendance

Present

Absent

week of:

Songs

Verse

Lesson

Craft and Activity

attendance

Present

Absent

week of:

Songs

Verse

Lesson

Craft and Activity

attendance

Present

Absent

week of:

Songs

Verse

Lesson

Craft and Activity

attendance

Present

Absent

week of:

Songs

Verse

Lesson

Craft and Activity

attendance

Present

Absent

week of:

Songs

Verse

Lesson

Craft and Activity

attendance

Present

Absent

week of:

Songs

Verse

Lesson

Craft and Activity

attendance

Present

Absent

week of:

Songs

Verse

Lesson

Craft and Activity

attendance

Present

Absent

week of:

Songs

Verse

Lesson

Craft and Activity

attendance

Present

Absent

week of:

Songs

Verse

Lesson

Craft and Activity

attendance

Present

Absent

week of:

Songs

Verse

Lesson

Craft and Activity

attendance

Present

Absent

week of:

Songs

Verse

Lesson

Craft and Activity

attendance

Present

Absent

week of:

Songs

Verse

Lesson

Craft and Activity

attendance

Present

Absent

week of:

Songs

Verse

Lesson

Craft and Activity

attendance

Present

Absent

week of:

Songs

Verse

Lesson

Craft and Activity

attendance

Present

Absent

week of:

Songs

Verse

Lesson

Craft and Activity